THIS BOOK BELONG

_____

Frank The Farting Flamingo

by Humor Heals Us

Hi, I'm Frank.
People call me Frank the Farting Flamingo.
I'm not sure why.
Everyone farts.

The truth is farting is so common that we can even give them names.

See how many of these you have experienced...

The Silent Ninja

This one is sneaky. It comes out and no-one even knows because it's so silent.

But just because it's quiet doesn't mean it doesn't pack a smelly punch. It stinks...BAD!!!

Have you ever released a Silent Ninja?

The Hot Biscuit

This deadly air biscuit is too hot and thick to produce sound. It just creates a really bad odor.

The Butt Putt

This fart is sort of cute and could easily be mistaken for someone popping their bubble gum.

The Grenade

This is probably the LOUDEST of all farts. At first you hear a loud BOOM! And then, the shockwaves come rushing in and you have to leave the room.

Ever released a Grenade before?

The Running Fart

This one happens when you're well... running. It is the fart that slowly escapes with every step you take, like the slow release of a balloon. In order to not let it all go, you might intentionally run slower.

The Car Ride Fart

This is the fart where everyone gets mad at you. It can happen on the way to school, on the ride home, or right before practice. You didn't mean it. So you argue that research indicates it's much healthier to release gas than to hold it in.

The Party Fart

The Party Fart got its name by its very potent odor, strong enough to make quite a few people look around. The trick here is not to identify the fart but the farter.

Eeeeww...

This is almost impossible unless the farter panics, and starts a fit of coughing or starts staring at the ceiling or the sky as though something up there fascinates him. In which case, he is the one. Super common.

So you see? You may have experienced one or more of these kinds of farts which makes you a Farting Flamingo, too...

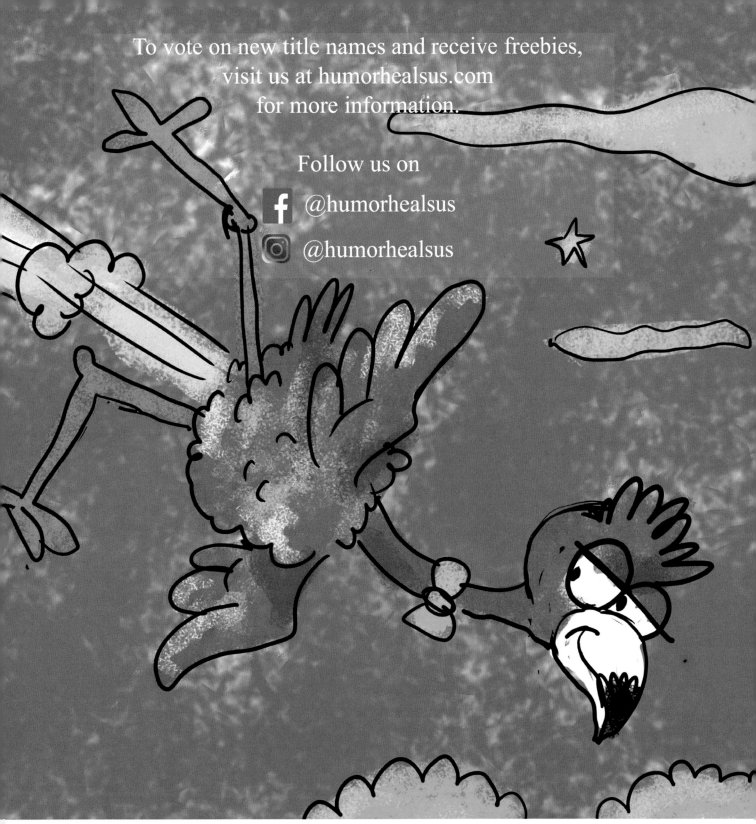

To vote on new title names and receive freebies,
visit us at humorhealsus.com
for more information.

Follow us on
@humorhealsus
@humorhealsus

Made in the USA
Las Vegas, NV
10 November 2023